F or E♭ Horns

Super
Duets

Philip Sparke

© 2011 by **Anglo Music Press**
PO Box 303, Wembley, HA9 8GX, England
Copyright secured / All rights reserved

SUPER DUETS
F or E♭ Horns
Philip Sparke

Order Number: AMP 330-401
ISMN: 979-0-57029-330-8

Printed in the EU

Contents

About this edition

The structured acquisition of new skills is undoubtedly an important factor when learning any wind instrument. A good teacher is of course essential but it is also vital to have stimulating pieces to play, which complement your choice of teaching method, and are carefully tailored to introduce learning and playing skills in a logical manner.

As with the previous books in this series, these duets introduce new musical elements in a logical order to facilitate the speedy growth of the 'complete musician', with the obvious benefit of allowing teacher and student (or two students) to play together and therefore experience the benefits of ensemble playing as part of the learning process.

So, may I wish you lots of fun with these duets as you continue your journey in the world of music!

Enjoy!

Philip Sparke

 Philip Sparke was born in London in 1951 and studied composition, trumpet and piano at the Royal College of Music, where he gained an ARCM.

It was at the College that his interest in writing instrumental music arose, alongside his compositions for concert band and brass band. He studied trumpet with Bob Walton who encouraged him to write his own studies for the instrument, as well as brass and wind chamber music for various student performing groups.

His solo pieces for brass and woodwind instruments have appeared in the syllabuses of all the various UK examination boards and this led him to compiling scale books and being commissioned to write sight-reading exercises and recital pieces for the major syllabuses in the UK.

He regularly adjudicates at music festivals around the UK and has travelled to most European countries, Australia, New Zealand, Japan and the USA.

He runs his own publishing company, *Anglo Music Press*, which he formed in May 2000. In September 2000 he was awarded the Iles Medal of the Worshipful Company of Musicians for his services to brass bands.

SUPER DUETS
15 Duets for F or E♭ Horns

1. Let's Tune

Philip Sparke

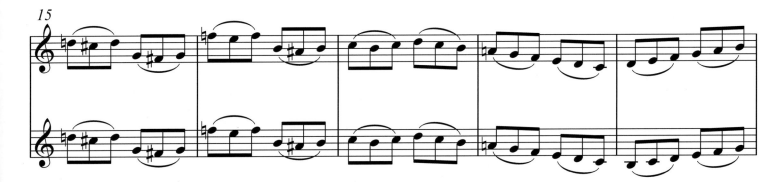

2. Follow the Leader

Philip Sparke

3. All Change

Philip Sparke

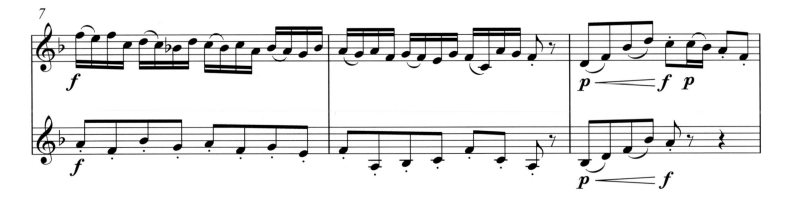

4. Mountain Air

Philip Sparke

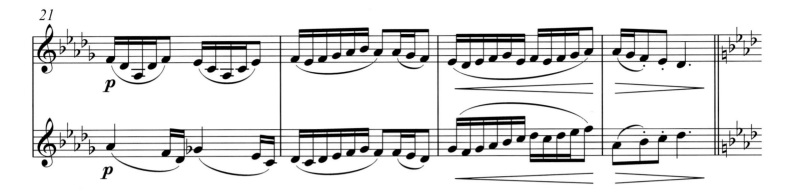

5. Moto Perpetuo

Philip Sparke

Ritmico

6. Morning Song

Philip Sparke

Andantino

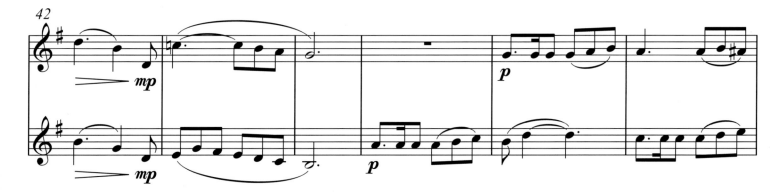

7. March of the Toys

Philip Sparke

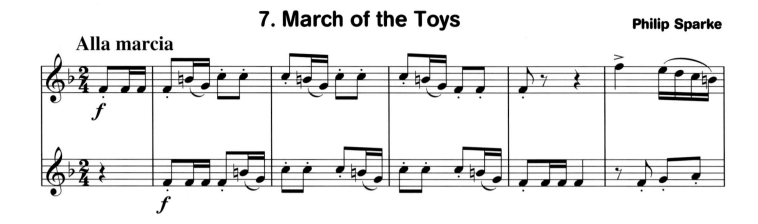

8. Wish You Were Here

Philip Sparke

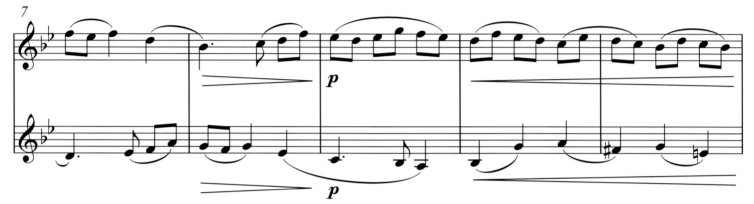

9. Circus March

Philip Sparke

10. Build Your Tone

Philip Sparke

Moderato

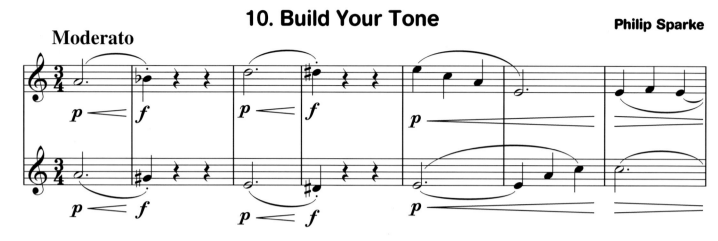

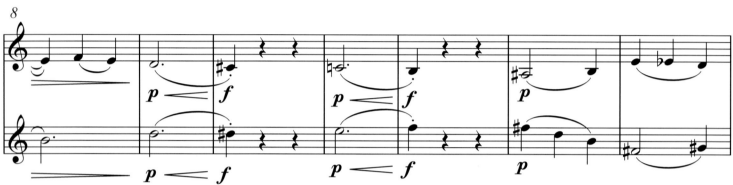

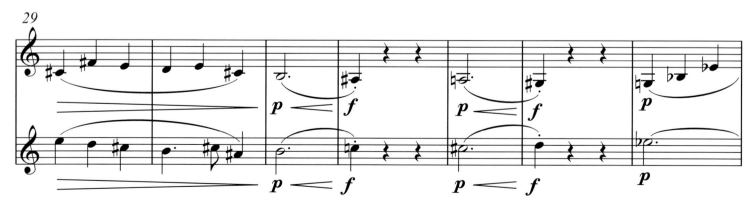

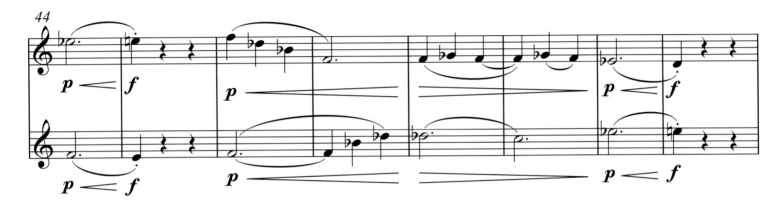

11. Be Flexible!

Philip Sparke

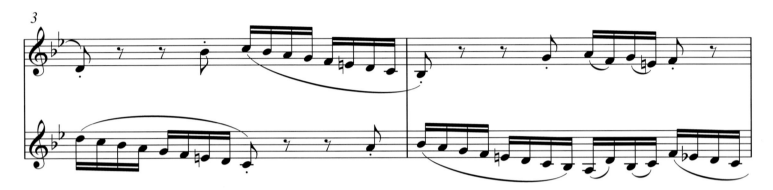

12. Lyric Piece

Philip Sparke

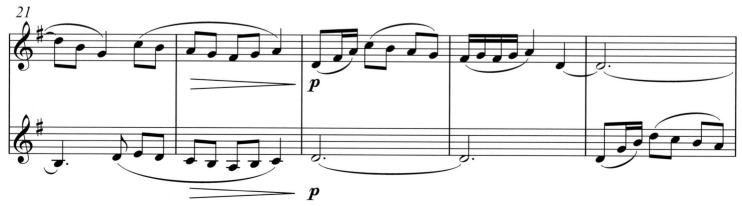

13. Canon

Philip Sparke

Moderato

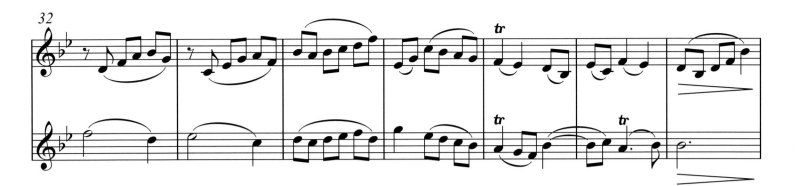

14. Time for a Change

Philip Sparke

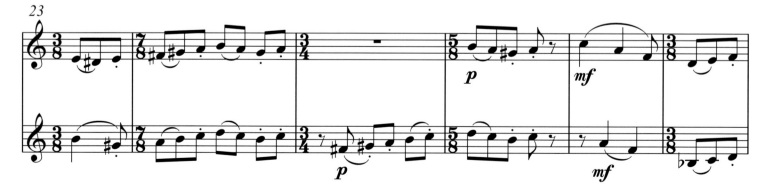

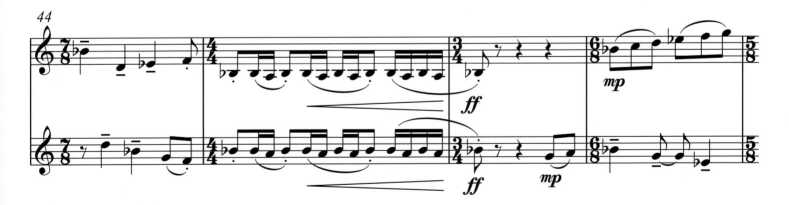

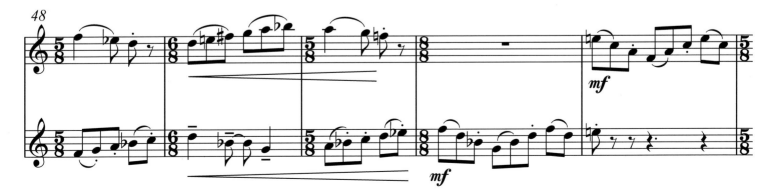

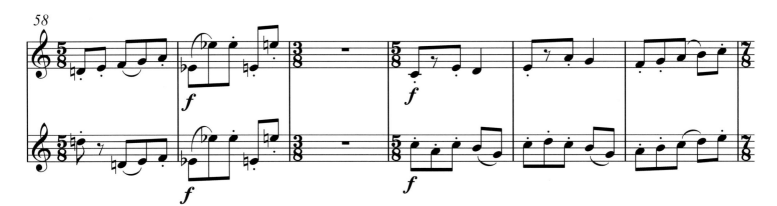

15. Toccata Variations

Philip Sparke

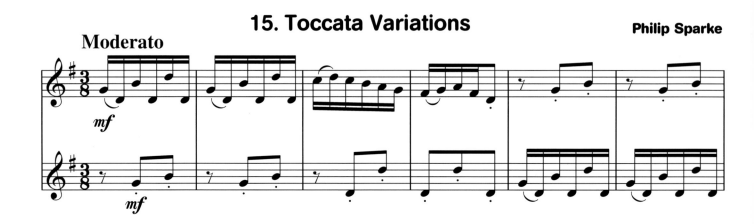

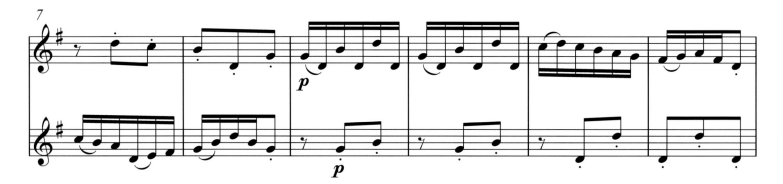

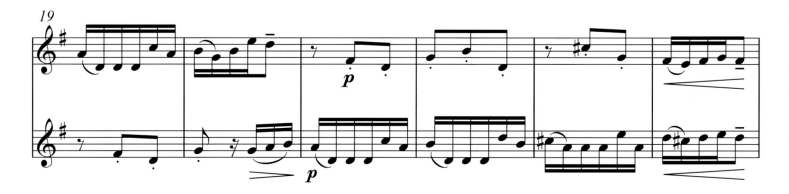

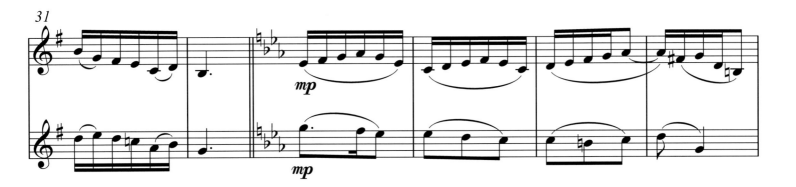

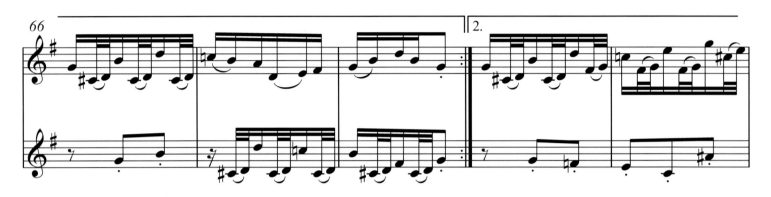

Über diese Ausgabe

Der strukturierte Erwerb neuer Fertigkeiten ist zweifellos ein sehr wichtiger Faktor beim Erlernen eines jeden Blasinstruments. Ein guter Lehrer ist natürlich ebenso unverzichtbar, aber auch anregende Spielstücke sind elementar, die genau auf Ihre Unterrichtsmethode abgestimmt und zugleich sorgfältig darauf zugeschnitten sind, Theorie und Spielfertigkeiten sinnvoll zu vermitteln.

Gleichermaßen wie die Stücke in den bereits erschienen Büchern dieser Reihe, führen die Duette in diesem Buch neue musikalische Elemente in einer logischen Reihenfolge ein, um das schnelle Heranreifen der Schüler zu „vollendeten Musikern" zu fördern, verbunden mit dem klaren Nutzen, der in der Möglichkeit des Zusammenspiels von Lehrer und Schüler (oder von zwei Schülern) liegt. So werden schon im frühen Lernstadium wichtige Erfahrungen im Ensemblespiel gesammelt.

Nun will ich allen, die ihren Weg in der Welt der Musik fortsetzen, noch viel Spaß mit diesen Duetten wünschen!

Genießt es!

Philip Sparke

 Philip Sparke wurde 1951 in London geboren. Er studierte Komposition, Trompete und Klavier am Royal College of Music und wurde dort als ARCM (Associate of the Royal College of Music) ausgezeichnet.

Zu dieser Zeit erwachte sein Interesse, parallel zu Kompositionen für Blasorchester und Brass Bands, auch Instrumentalmusik zu schreiben. Er studierte Trompete bei Bob Walton, der ihn ermutigte, eigene Etüden für dieses Instrument und Kammermusik für Bläser und Blechbläser für verschiedene Studentenensembles zu schreiben.

Philip Sparkes Solostücke für Blech- und Holzbläser wurden in die Lehrpläne aller unterschiedlichen Prüfungsausschüsse Großbritanniens aufgenommen. Dies führte dazu, dass er Skalenbücher zusammenstellte und beauftragt wurde, Vom Blatt-Leseübungen und Konzertstücke für die wichtigsten Lehrpläne Großbritanniens zu schreiben.

Regelmäßig ist er als Berater bei Musikfestivals in Großbritannien tätig. Seine Reisen führten ihn in die meisten europäischen Länder, nach Australien, Neuseeland, Japan und in die USA.

Philip Sparke leitet einen eigenen Musikverlag, *Anglo Music Press*, gegründet im Mai 2000. Im September 2000 erhielt er die Iles Medal of the Worshipful Company of Music für seine Verdienste um den Brass Band-Bereich.

À propos de cette édition

L'acquisition structurée de nouvelles compétences est sans aucun doute un facteur important lors de l'apprentissage de tout instrument à vent. Un bon professeur est un élément-clé, mais il est tout aussi important de pouvoir disposer d'un répertoire adapté et complémentaire à la méthode d'enseignement utilisée. Vous serez alors judicieusement amené à optimiser vos compétences en suivant un parcours coordonné et logique.

À l'instar de l'ensemble des volumes d'études et duos instrumentaux de cette collection, *Super Duets* fera de vous un "musicien complet". L'écoute de soi et des autres, la justesse et la régularité du tempo seront des notions abordées grâce au jeu en ensemble (avec votre professeur ou un autre élève).

Donc, je vous souhaite beaucoup de plaisir et un agréable voyage dans le monde merveilleux de la musique !

Amusez-vous !

Philip Sparke

Né en 1951 à Londres, Philip Sparke étudie la composition, la trompette et le piano au prestigieux Collège Royal de Musique de Londres où il obtient l'Associate Diploma (ARCM).

Il se découvre un intérêt pour la composition de musique instrumentale et d'œuvres pour Orchestre d'Harmonie et Brass Band alors qu'il fréquente le Collège Royal. Sous l'impulsion de son professeur de trompette, Bob Walton, Philip Sparke compose des études pour trompette et des pièces de musique de chambre pour instruments à vent (bois / cuivres) destinées à divers ensembles instrumentaux.

Ses pièces solos pour cuivres et bois figurent au répertoire des œuvres de concours et d'examens nationaux du Royaume-Uni. Il rédigera par la suite plusieurs recueils de gammes. De nombreuses commandes de pièces de récital et d'exercices de lecture à vue lui parviennent alors, notamment du comité chargé des principaux programmes éducatifs nationaux.

Philip Sparke est un membre de jury très sollicité lors de concours et d'événements nationaux ou dans la plupart des pays d'Europe, en Australie, en Nouvelle-Zélande, au Japon et aux États-Unis.

Depuis mai 2000, il publie ses compositions sous son label *Anglo Music Press*. En septembre 2000, l'association britannique Worshipful Company of Musicians le récompense de la prestigieuse Iles Medal pour son engagement en faveur des Brass Bands.

Over deze uitgave

De gestructureerde verwerving van nieuwe vaardigheden is zonder twijfel een belangrijke factor bij het leren bespelen van een blaasinstrument. Een goede docent is natuurlijk essentieel, maar eveneens van groot belang is het gebruik van motiverend speelmateriaal dat de keuze voor een leermethode aanvult en zorgvuldig is toegesneden op een logisch opgebouwde introductie van leer- en speelvaardigheden.

Net als de stukken uit de voorgaande boeken in deze serie introduceren de duetten in dit boek nieuwe muzikale elementen in een doordachte volgorde, om de ontwikkeling van de complete muzikant te bevorderen. Bijkomend voordeel is uiteraard dat de docent en leerling (of twee leerlingen) samen kunnen spelen, zodat het ensemblespel al vroeg in het leerproces aan de orde komt.

Rest mij nog iedereen veel speelgenoegen te wensen met deze duetten tijdens de verdere ontdekkingsreis in de fantastische wereld van de muziek.

Veel plezier!

Philip Sparke

Philip Sparke werd in 1951 in Londen geboren en studeerde compositie, trompet en piano aan het Royal College of Music, waar hij het ARCM-diploma haalde (Associate of the Royal College of Music).

Tijdens deze opleiding groeide zijn belangstelling voor het schrijven van instrumentale muziek, naast zijn composities voor harmonieorkest en brassband. Hij studeerde trompet bij Bob Walton, die hem aanmoedigde om zijn eigen etudes voor dit instrument te schrijven, evenals muziek voor brassband en blaasensemble voor diverse studentengroepen.

Zijn solostukken voor koper- en houtinstrumenten zijn verschenen in de leerplannen van alle verschillende examencommissies van Groot-Brittannië; dit bracht hem ertoe om boeken met toonladderstudies samen te stellen. Bovendien schreef hij in opdracht oefeningen voor het spelen van blad en speelstukken voor de belangrijkste leerplannen in Groot-Brittannië.

Philip Sparke zit regelmatig in jury's van muziekfestivals in Groot-Brittannië en zijn dirigeer- en juryactiviteiten brachten hem naar de meeste Europese landen, Australië, Nieuw-Zeeland, Japan en de Verenigde Staten.

Hij publiceert zijn eigen werken onder zijn eigen label, *Anglo Music Press*, opgericht in mei 2000. In september 2000 ontving hij de Iles Medal of the Worshipful Company of Musicians voor zijn bewezen diensten aan brassbands.